Janos Molnar. Born 1932 in Budapest. Degree in literature. A young journalist for the party organ Szabad Nep during the events of 1956. After the Hungarian uprising was put down, he helped reorganize the party police, in particular their dealings with intellectuals. Resided in Moscow 1959-1967. Molnar was made Vice Minister of the Interior on his return. Specialists believe his role in affairs of state far exceeds his official functions.

Ion Nicolescu. Born 1918 in the Danube delta. Little is known about his life until 1945 when he returned from Russia with the «muscovite» faction Georghiu-Dej. As a member of the Securitate, or political police, he oversaw the 1951 purges, but was himself purged in 1952 and placed under house arrest for five years. After a new round of purges he re-emerged, and for the last several years has been traveling widely as the chief spokesman for Rumanian diplomacy. He has been on the Central Committee since 1970, and again holds a high position in the Securitate. Considered an «up-and-comer» by experts.

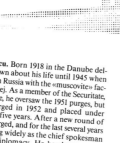

Tadeusz Boczek. Born 1914 in Wilno. Son of a rabbi. Degree in philosophy. Boczek entered the Polish Communist Party at 16 and rose to prominence as both theoretician and organizer. When the Komintern dissolved the party in 1938, he narrowly escaped execution. Underground work during World War II. Boczek became a full member of the politburo where he was a major ideological contributor until 1967, when he was forced out, a victim of the wave of anti-Semitism stirred up partly to mask the regime's economic failings. He appears to have disappeared from the political scene altogether.

Vasil Stroganov. Born 1920 or 1921. Peasant background. A partisan leader in the Rhodopes noted for his valor in the Bulgarian resistance, he was part of the first Dimitrov government 1946-47. Discredited for «Titoism,» Stroganov was rehabilitated in 1956 and placed in charge of the «Great Leap Forward» for the peasantry. The program was a failure. After a stint as ambassador to Switzerland, his sole post—largely honorific—has been head of the Front for Fatherland, or internal propaganda bureau. His prestige remains high among the masses.

Pavel Havelka. Born 1915 in the Prague suburbs. A social democrat before the «Prague coup» in 1948. His real sympathies lay with the Communist Party, which tapped him to serve in the Gottwald government. Arrested and sentenced for «bourgeois nationalism» during the Slansky trial (1951). Freed in 1963 and named Minister of Culture, he appeared to be a liberal, actively contributing to the dynamics of the «Prague spring». After Czechoslovakia was crushed, Havelka was unconcerned and helped take the country in hand again, establishing ties with the Party's centrist faction, where he plays a key role.

Evgeny Golozov. Born 1918 in the Ukraine. Working class origins, joined the Party while very young. Attended the University of Moscow to study languages (French, English, German, Rumanian, Hungarian, slavic languages). Much decorated for acts of bravery during World War II, wounded several times. Apart from the foregoing, little is known of Golozov's career, always in the shadow of his mentor, Vassili Chevchenko. Golozov is a member of the Central Committee.

Günther Schütz. Born 1930 in Leipzig. Father a career military man. Studied philosophy, then economics. Has been known for his scientific articles since 1955. Schütz was among the most ardent advocates of building the Berlin Wall in 1961. Named an advisor to the East German politburo, he took a strong stand in favor of purging the Writers' Association and opposed the rehabilitation of «bourgeois» artists. From 1965 on, he was in charge of higher education for the Party in East Germany. Named to the COMECON in 1970, where he has played a major role since 1976. Schütz is the author of numerous works translated into most Eastern and Central European languages.

Also available by Enki Bilal:

Exterminator 17
with J.—P. Dionnet
ISBN 0-87416-024-3

Gods in Chaos
ISBN 0-87416-049-9

The Woman Trap
ISBN 0-87416-050-2

The Town That Didn't Exist
with P. Christin
ISBN 0-87416-051-0

**The Ranks of the Black
   Order**
with P. Christin
ISBN 0-87416-052-9

Other books of interest:

The Magician's Wife
Jerome Charyn/François Boucq
ISBN 0-87416-045-6

Joe's Bar
José Muñoz/Carlos Sampayo
ISBN 0-87416-046-4

Fires
Lorenzo Mattotti
ISBN 0-87416-048-0

**«Good-Bye» and Other
   Stories**
Yoshihiro Tatsumi
ISBN 0-87416-056-1

Love Shots
Jacques de Loustal/
   Philippe Paringaux
ISBN 0-87416-059-6

**Pioneers of the
   Human Adventure**
François Boucq
ISBN 0-87416-075-8'

BILAL & CHRISTIN
THE HUNTING PARTY

Translated by
ELIZABETH BELL

catalan communications
new york

«You've grown accustomed to power,
like bloody meat.»
          GYÖRGY KONRÀD

THE HUNTING PARTY
ISBN 0-87416-053-7

Story by Pierre Christin
Art by Enki Bilal

Translated from the French,
   "Partie de Chasse," by
   Elizabeth Bell
Edited by Bernd Metz

Published by Catalan Communications
   43 East 19th Street
   New York, NY 10003

© 1990 LES HUMANOIDES ASSOCIES

English language edition © 1990
   Catalan Communications

First Catalan Communications Edition
   February 1990

10 9 8 7 6 5 4 3 2 1

Printed in Catalonia (Spain)
Dep. L.B. 41.674/89

Write to us for a free catalogue of
   our graphic novels.

5

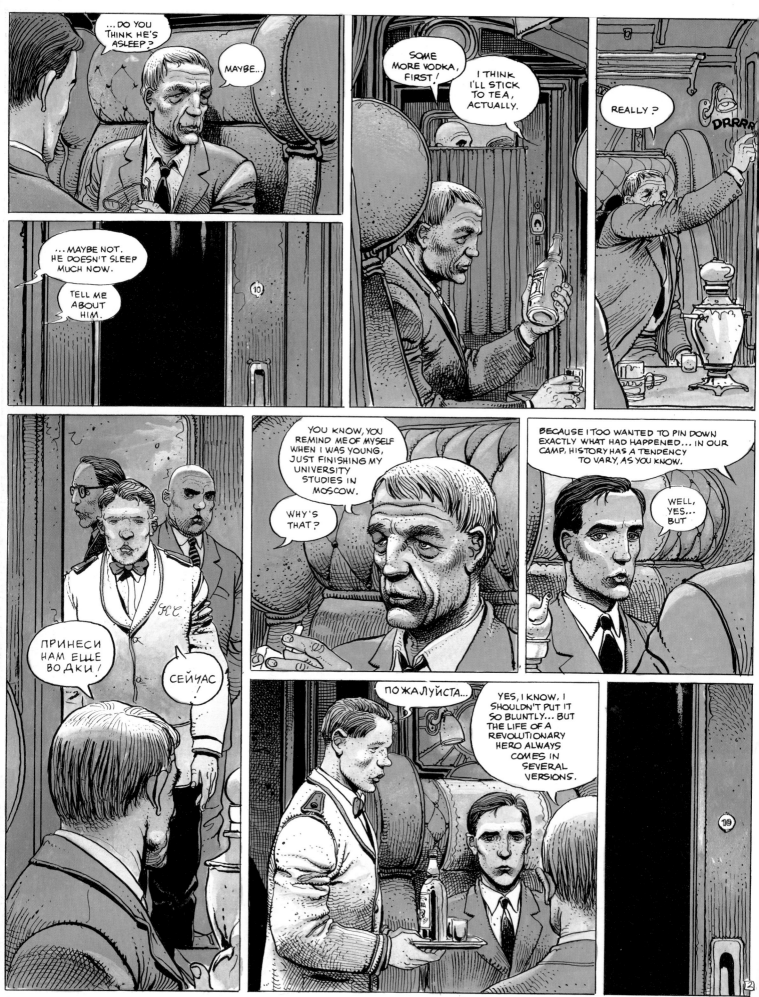

6

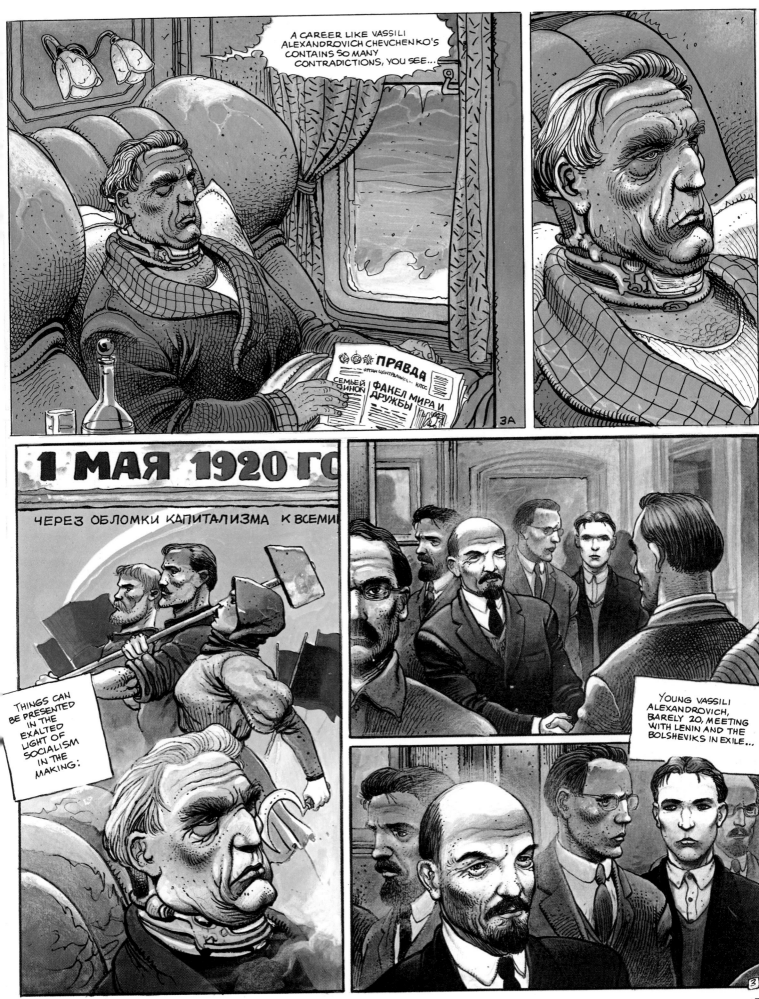

... PARTICIPATING IN THE PETROGRAD SOVIET, THE STORMING OF THE WINTER PALACE ONE FALL EVENING IN 1917...

...THE FIRST DIVISIONS OF THE RED ARMY FORMING TO COMBAT THE REGIME'S ENEMIES – INTERNAL AND EXTERNAL...

...VASSILI ALEXANDROVICH ALWAYS SPOKE TO ME ABOUT HIS MOST VALIANT SOLDIER, AN AGELESS MUZHIK NAMED ZHUCHENKO...

WHOLE REGIONS FENDING OFF STARVATION, SUPPLY TRAINS ATTACKED AND PILLAGED BEFORE THEY COULD REACH THE TOWNS...

...THE CREATION OF A NEW NATION ON THE RUINS OF THE CZAR'S EMPIRE...

THE MASSIVE TASK OF MOBILIZING A VAST COUNTRY FOR INDUSTRIALIZATION AND TECHNOLOGY...

ПОМНИ ГОЛОДАЮЩИХ

9

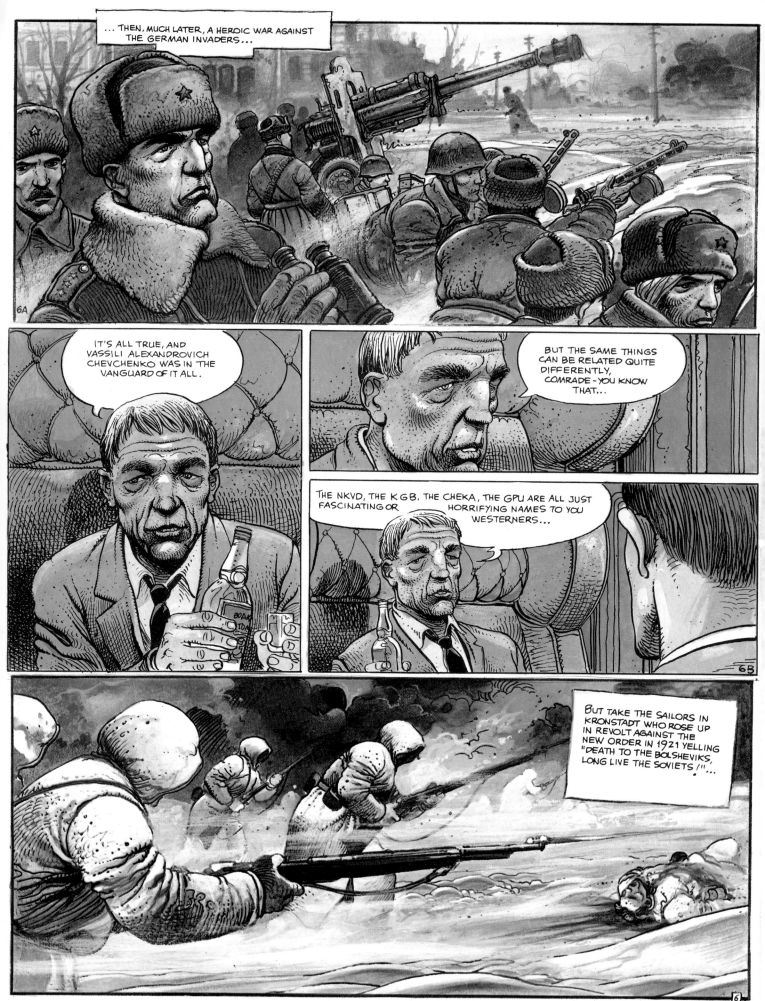

... THEN, MUCH LATER, A HEROIC WAR AGAINST THE GERMAN INVADERS...

IT'S ALL TRUE, AND VASSILI ALEXANDROVICH CHEVCHENKO WAS IN THE VANGUARD OF IT ALL.

BUT THE SAME THINGS CAN BE RELATED QUITE DIFFERENTLY, COMRADE - YOU KNOW THAT...

THE NKVD, THE K G B, THE CHEKA, THE GPU ARE ALL JUST FASCINATING OR HORRIFYING NAMES TO YOU WESTERNERS...

BUT TAKE THE SAILORS IN KRONSTADT WHO ROSE UP IN REVOLT AGAINST THE NEW ORDER IN 1921 YELLING "DEATH TO THE BOLSHEVIKS, LONG LIVE THE SOVIETS !"...

...OR THE INDEPENDENT GEORGIANS AND ALL THE OTHER NATIONALITIES FORCED INTO THE UNION AGAINST THEIR WILL...

...OR THE MUZHIKS, MOWED DOWN WHEN THEY DESPERATELY REBELLED AGAINST FORCED COLLECTIVIZATION...

... TAKE THE PURGE VICTIMS, WHO WERE ARRESTED, DEPORTED OR SHOT - OR "COMMITTED SUICIDE"...

...OR THE OLD GUARD REVOLUTIONARIES BRANDED AS TRAITORS DURING THE SWEEPING TRIALS HELD IN THE THIRTIES...

HE ALWAYS USED TO TALK ABOUT HIS GRANDFATHER. MAYBE HIS STRONGEST INFLUENCE...

MAXIM MAXIMOVICH CHEVCHENKO--A FAMOUS SPOKESMAN FOR THE PRO-SLAV INTELLIGENTSIA IN THE MID-19TH CENTURY.

A GENEROUS MAN...

...AND VERY RELIGIOUS, FULL OF ANTI-WESTERN FIRE AND BRIMSTONE, WITH A MESSIANIC BELIEF IN RUSSIA.

HE WAS HORRIFIED BY THE POVERTY OF THE MASSES, BUT LATER HE ENDED UP TAKING REFUGE IN A FINE LANDOWNER'S MANSION HE'D COME INTO BY MARRIAGE.

He still subsidized the rising social democracy—and he kept on telling stories to young Vassili Alexandrovich, whose father had died prematurely.

Strange tales, about the customs of our distant ancestors. When their king died, they had the whole court impaled...

Jesters, knights and ladies in their court gowns, all on stakes like pieces on a gigantic chess board...

18

20

25

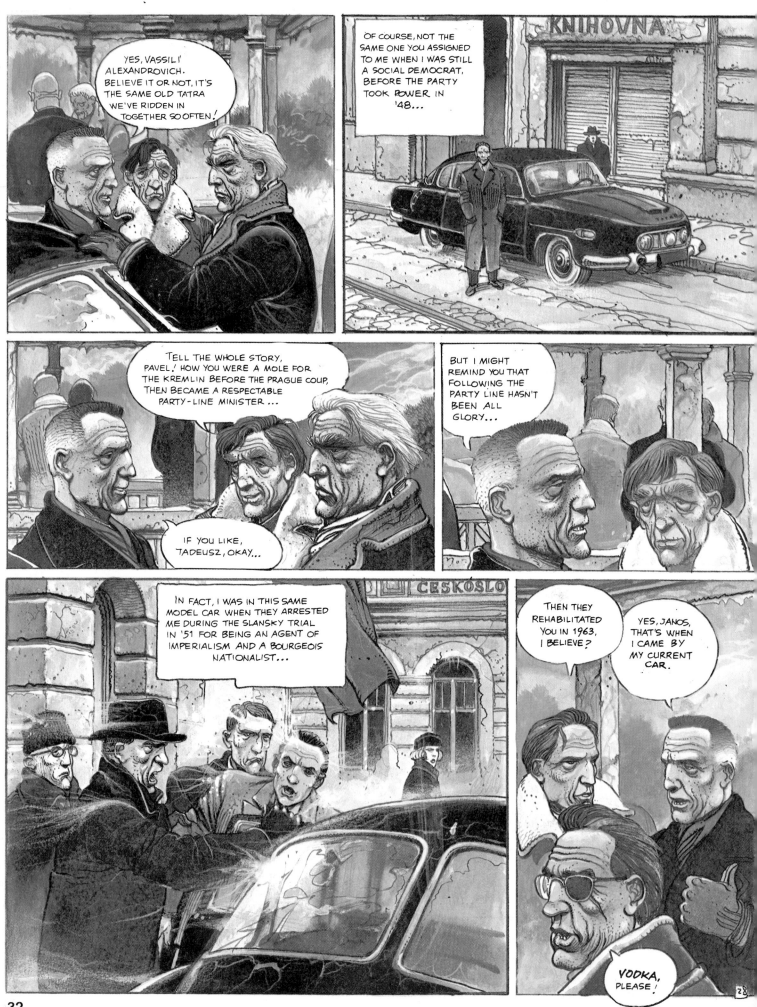

A MEMENTO OF A GOOD TIME... BUT THE WHOLE PERIOD WAS A GOOD TIME, WOULDN'T YOU SAY VASSILI ALEXANDROVICH?

REMEMBER WHEN YOU WENT WITH ME TO THE MINISTRY OF CULTURE TO WORK OUT AN UNDERSTANDING BETWEEN THE INTELLECTUALS AND THE PARTY?

EXCEPT FOR THAT DOLT VIZEK WHO KEPT ASKING WHO WAS INFILTRATING WHAT, IT WENT BEAUTIFULLY.

BUT I'M SURE YOU ALSO RECALL OUR MEETING NEAR THE BORDER ON AUGUST 15, 1968...

IN THE FRONT SEAT OF THIS CAR, YOU WARNED ME THE PACT TROOPS MIGHT ACTUALLY INVADE.

I DIDN'T BELIEVE IT-ANY MORE THAN DUBČEK DID... WE JUST DROVE AND DROVE ALONG THE LITTLE MOUNTAIN ROADS, SAYING NOTHING...

29

33

35

SHIT! MISSED.

YOU SEE, OUR FRENCH COMRADE, THEY'RE NOT ALL CHAMPIONS.

THEY'RE ALL BETTER THAN ME, THAT'S FOR SURE!

THE SUN'S GOING DOWN, ANYWAY... IT'S TIME WE GOT BACK.

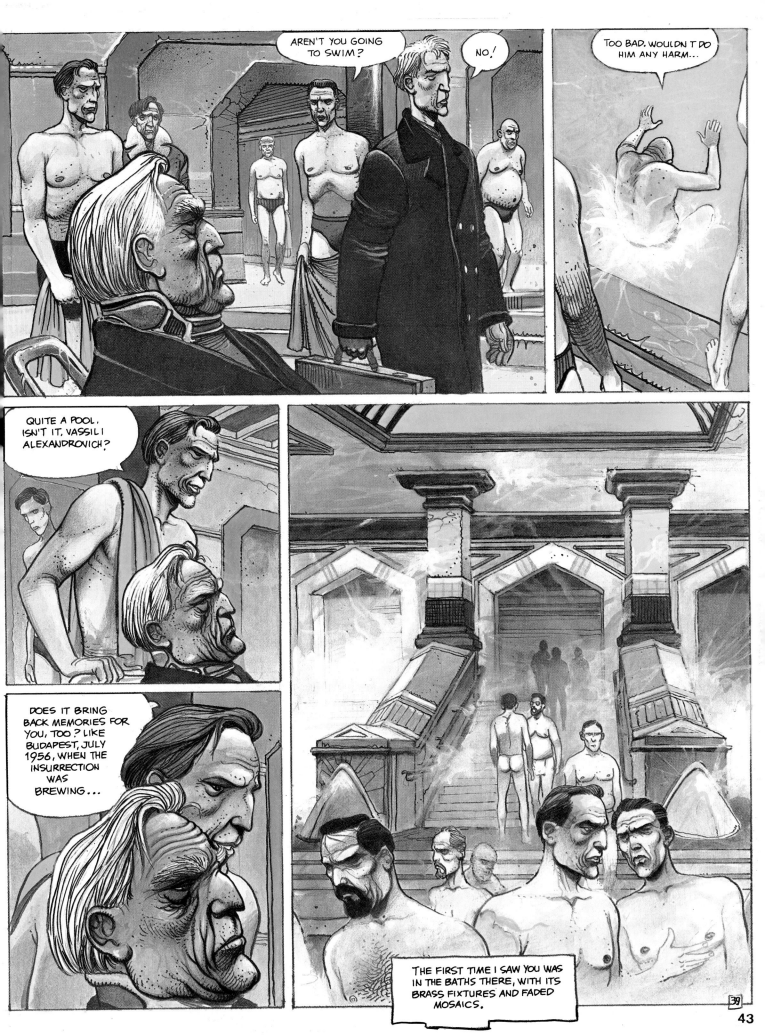

ASTOUNDING WORDS, NO DOUBT, TO A LONG-TIME MILITANT WHO'D BEEN POSITIVELY DEVOTED TO YOU FOR SO MANY YEARS...

THEN EVERYONE HEADED TO THE STEAM ROOM, WITH EVEN DENSER HEAT AND MIST.

SILENCE REIGNED, EACH ONE PONDERING THE EVENTS YOU HOPED TO AVERT BY REVAMPING A LEADERSHIP THE PEOPLE DESPISED.

IT WASN'T UNTIL THE GROUP WAS ABOUT TO DISPERSE INTO INDIVIDUAL CUBICLES FOR A MASSAGE THAT I NOTICED SOMEONE WAS MISSING...

TIBOR, YOUR VASSAL FALLEN FROM GRACE... I WENT BACK TO THE DESERTED POOL, FILLED WITH THE ODOR OF LINIMENT AND UNSEEN MOULD...

...AND DISCOVERED THE BODY FLOATING QUIETLY IN THE WATER... SUICIDE? HEART ATTACK? NO ONE EVER KNEW.

WAS IT BECAUSE I WAS THE ONE TO NOTIFY YOU OF THE TRAGEDY THAT YOU STRUCK UP A FRIENDSHIP WITH ME?

THE NEXT TIME YOU CAME TO OUR CAPITAL, THERE WAS FIGHTING IN THE STREETS... I'VE OFTEN WONDERED WHY YOU PICKED ME, OUT OF ALL THE OTHERS.

OF COURSE, I HADN'T TAKEN PART IN THE REBELLION, MAYBE YOU TOOK THIS AS STRATEGY ON MY PART ...

... BUT WHEN YOU CALLED ME IN TO HELP REVAMP THE PARTY POLICE AFTER THE CRACKDOWN ...

... AND ALL THE WHILE I WAS SERVING MY POLITICAL APPRENTICESHIP AT YOUR SIDE IN MOSCOW...

... I OFTEN REFLECTED THAT MAYBE MY CHANCE DISCOVERY OF YOUR FRIEND'S DEATH LED YOU TO REPLACE HIM WITH ME.

DINNER, GENTLEMEN!

CCCP ОПЛОТ МИРА

TIBOR ILLYES 1891 - 1956

42

48

ABOUT THE PAST, PROBABLY...

...AS HE OFTEN DOES.

BUT FOR HIM THERE ARE SO MANY PASTS...

...INTERTWINED, CONTRADICTORY PASTS...

...BUT EVEN SO, VASSILI ALEXANDROVICH REMAINS A MAN OF THE PRESENT.

HE MAY EVEN BE PROJECTING INTO THE FUTURE. DON'T WE ALL?

— O.K., GOOD NIGHT, KID.
— GOOD NIGHT, EVGENY.

46

51

52

48

54

THE KOMINTERN HAD JUST DISSOLVED OUR PARTY, SUPPOSEDLY FOR TROTSKYISM, AND A HUNDRED OF OUR LEADERS HAD BEEN LIQUIDATED IN MOSCOW...

...I SHOULD HAVE BEEN AMONG THEM...

BUT VASSILI ALEXANDROVICH, THINKING OF THE FUTURE, SHIPPED ME OUT ON SOME LEAKY TUB ACROSS THE BLACK SEA TO ISTANBUL.

WHEN THE FIRST GERMAN BOMB FELL ON WARSAW IN SEPTEMBER OF '39, I HAD SECRETLY RETURNED—AT HIS REQUEST ...

BUT I CHOSE TO REMAIN ALONGSIDE MY PEOPLE, AS A JEW AS WELL AS A COMMUNIST, WHEN THE NAZIS BEGAN TO LIQUIDATE THE "UNTERMENSCHEN"...

THE WARSAW GHETTO! FIVE HUNDRED THOUSAND PEOPLE... TWO HUNDRED SURVIVORS. ONE OF THEM ME...

BUILDINGS TORCHED BY FLAME-THROWER, CHILDREN BURNED ALIVE, PARENTS KILLING THEIR CHILDREN TO SPARE THEM THE HORROR...

CARTLOADS OF CORPSES, DAY AFTER DAY, A CITY IN RUINS, THE STENCH OF ROTTING FLESH... I LIVED THROUGH IT ALL.

DURING THE GHETTO UPRISING IN 1943, WHEN THE S.S. WAS BLOWING UP EVERYTHING IN SIGHT, VASSILI ALEXANDROVICH AGAIN STEPPED IN AND ARRANGED MY ESCAPE. THE PARTY WAS LEADERLESS AND HAD TO BE RECONSTITUTED; THEY PREFERRED TO KEEP ME ALIVE.

AFTER THE WAR, HE AND I WALKED THROUGH THAT IMMENSE CHARNEL-HOUSE REEKING OF CARRION FROM UNDER THE RUBBLE. WE TALKED OF OUR DREAMS FOR RECONSTRUCTING MY POOR NATION...

THEN TODAY, AS YOU ALL SAW...

VASSILI ALEXANDROVICH RENEWED MY VISA FOR THIS PLANET.'

HERE'S TO THE THREE LIVES I OWE HIM.'

WHAT ABOUT THE DEATHS?

THE FIRST ONE WAS ALSO IN ODESSA...WHERE A LITTLE JEW FROM WILNO HAD HIS FIRST DOUBTS ABOUT THE "HOMELAND OF SOCIALISM," WHICH SEEMED BENT ON DESTROYING THE MOST DEDICATED COMMUNIST MILITANTS IN OTHER COUNTRIES.

THE SECOND GOES BACK TO THE END OF THE WAR...

I'D BECOME A RANKING MEMBER OF WARSAW'S POLITBURO, AND ONE OF MY DUTIES WAS TO MONITOR THE CONSTRUCTION OF A CULTURAL CENTER THE SOVIETS BESTOWED ON THE MARTYRED POLISH PEOPLE.

I SOON LEARNED THE PRICE YOU PAY YOUR GENEROUS BUT DEMANDING PROTECTOR, THE CONFIDENT, RIGID ELDER BROTHER, THE CRUEL OGRE THAT DEVOURS ITS OWN CHILDREN... AND I KNEW SHAME...

55

BUT I DIDN'T FULLY GRASP THINGS UNTIL MY THIRD DEATH IN 1967, MY POLITICAL DEATH. VASSILI ALEXANDROVICH HIMSELF GAVE ME THE NEWS, IN THE HALLS OF THAT SAME CULTURAL CENTER I'D HELPED BRING INTO BEING...

THE REGIME NEEDED SCAPEGOATS FOR ITS FAILINGS. SO WHOM DID THEY PICK ON? THE FEW JEWS WHO'D MADE IT THROUGH THE GERMAN GENOCIDE, METICULOUS AS IT WAS...

EVERYONE WAS UP IN ARMS AGAINST THE "MOSZKI DO PALESTINY"–"MOSESES OF PALESTINE"– AND I, TADEUSZ BOCZEK, WAS FORCED OUT, THOUGH FORTUNATE ENOUGH TO BE RETIRED TO THIS FAROFF COUNTRY–THANKS TO VASSILI ALEXANDROVICH, ONCE AGAIN.

SO, FRIENDS, THAT'S THE STORY OF MY THREE LIVES AND THREE DEATHS.

SERGEI SHAVANIDZE IS ONLY HALFWAY SURPRISED BY MR. BOCZEK'S CONSISTENTLY ANTI-SOVIET TONE...

...AND NOTES THAT VASSILI ALEXANDROVICH NEVER DID HAVE GOOD LUCK WITH HIS MEN IN WARSAW.

THAT'S VERY TRUE.

...NOR OF THE TIME I WAS IN THE DIMITROV ADMINISTRATION, WITH VASSILI ALEXANDROVICH'S BLESSING...

IT WAS NOT UNTIL I HAD BARELY ESCAPED HANGING, FOR TITOISM IT SEEMS, BEFORE I STARTED DREAMING.

VASSILI ALEXANDROVICH SAVED MY HIDE AND PUT ME IN CHARGE OF THE BULGARIAN PEASANTRY'S GREAT LEAP FORWARD, AS WE CALLED IT, IN '58.

BUT I'VE HAD THE SAME NIGHTMARE EVER SINCE...

...OF THIS VAGUE, OBSCENE MONSTER FROM SOME STAR THAT'S GONE DEAD SOMEWHERE...

AND SOMETIMES I THINK THE MONSTER IS ME, VASIL STROGANOV, OR MAYBE IT'S THE PARTY ITSELF, AND I'M JUST ITS RAVING MOUTH, OR ONE VICIOUS CLAW!

76

77

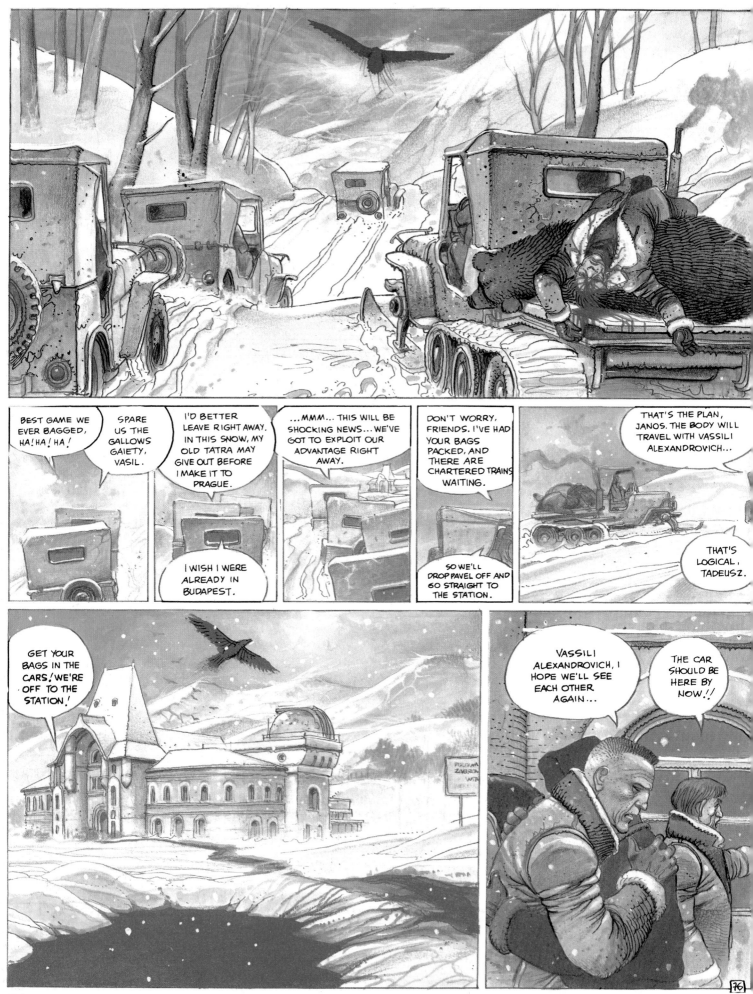

82